GREEN-VEINED WHITE p64

GR

HOLLY BLUE p70

LARGE BLUE p72

LARGE HEATH p74

LARGE SKIPPER p76

LARGE WHITE p78

MARBLED WHITE p80

THE LITTLE
BOOK *of*
BUTTERFLIES

First published in 2023 by Fine Feather Press Ltd
The Coach House, Elstead Road, Farnham, Surrey GU10 1JE
EU enquiries: Andrea Pinnington, 2022 Route de Laurélie
12270 Bor-et-Bar, France
Copyright © 2023 Fine Feather Press Ltd

2 4 6 8 10 9 7 5 3 1

A CIP catalogue record is available from the British Library
ISBN: 978-1-908489-65-4
Printed in China

Fine Feather Press makes every effort to ensure that the papers used in its books are made from
trees that have been legally sourced from well-managed and credibly certified forests.

www.finefeatherpress.com

THE LITTLE
BOOK *of*
BUTTERFLIES

A NEW WORLD
TO DISCOVER

Consultant: Dr Martin Warren OBE

CONTENTS

FOREWORD

by Dr Martin Warren OBE

Butterflies have a special place in our affections. Their graceful wings brighten warm summer days and bring joy to thousands of people every year. Their transformation from egg to caterpillar to chrysalis and adult is one of the wonders of nature. They are powerful symbols of freedom and happiness, and sum up the beauty and fragility of the natural world.

Just as importantly, butterflies give us a window on the vast world of insects, which play a vital role in the health of our environment. Without insects, most plants would not be pollinated and many ecosystems would quickly collapse. By studying butterflies, we can help understand the world around us and gain an insight into what makes it tick. Every observation adds to our knowledge of how populations are changing and how best to conserve them.

I first became fascinated by butterflies as a child, watching the different kinds that visited my parents' garden and rearing caterpillars at home. They have given me a lifetime of interest and enjoyment. I hope this book stimulates your own curiosity about these wonderful insects so you can experience the same thrills and delight that they have brought me.

A BUTTERFLY'S ANATOMY

LIKE ALL INSECTS, a butterfly's body has three parts: a head; a thorax to which two sets of wings and six legs are attached; and an abdomen. Below are the terms used in this book to describe different butterflies. It helps to know your forewings from your hindwings and your uppersides from your undersides.

Head

Forewing

Thorax

Hindwing

Abdomen

WING UPPERSIDES

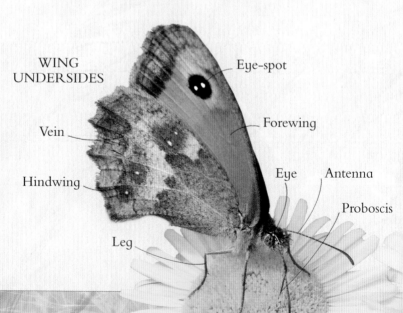

WING UNDERSIDES

Eye-spot

Vein

Forewing

Hindwing

Eye   Antenna

Proboscis

Leg

ANTENNAE

A butterfly's long feelers, or antennae, detect scents and help a butterfly to balance. There is also evidence to suggest that they monitor the sun, and so aid navigation.

EYES

Humans have one lens in each eye; butterflies have about 17,000! Such eyes are known as compound eyes, where the lenses work together in order to detect movement and light.

PROBOSCIS

A feeding tube or tongue called a proboscis sucks up nectar from flowers and other fluids such as sugary tree sap. The proboscis is tightly coiled to keep it out of the way when it is not being used.

VEINS

The wings are made up of two thin layers with veins running through them. When a butterfly emerges from a chrysalis, fluid runs through these veins, causing the wings to expand.

SCALES

The front and back of a butterfly's wings are covered with thousands of tiny overlapping scales – shown above in close-up. It is these scales that give the butterfly's wings their colour.

LEGS

As with all insects, butterflies have six legs. However, in the family of butterflies called Nymphalidae, the front pair of legs is tiny and only the rear two pairs are used for walking.

A BUTTERFLY'S LIFE CYCLE

A BUTTERFLY STARTS life as an egg. In order to reach adulthood, it has to go through four separate stages, transforming its shape and structure completely each time, in a process called metamorphosis.

The life cycle of many butterflies takes a year, which includes inhospitable weather conditions. To survive these, some butterflies spend the winter as inactive caterpillars and continue their life cycle in the spring. Others hibernate as eggs or chrysalises, and a few do so as adults.

Those butterflies with shorter life cycles may have two or three (occasionally four) generations in a single year. Each generation is known as a brood, and it is the final brood of the year that will need to overwinter in order to ensure the survival of the species.

EGG

The female lays her eggs on or near a plant on which her caterpillars feed when they hatch. The size and shape of the eggs varies between species – these being the bottle-shaped eggs of the large white. All eggs have a dimple through which air reaches the developing caterpillar inside.

CATERPILLAR

The caterpillar is tiny when it hatches out. It is born to eat and grow, sometimes doubling its size every few days. To make room for its expanding body, it has to shed its skin – usually about five times – until it is fully grown. Each new stage is called an instar.

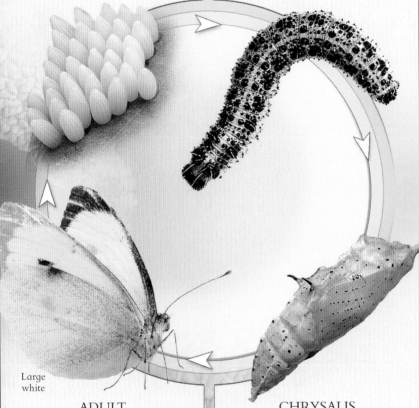

Large white

ADULT

When the adult butterfly is ready to emerge, it swallows air through holes in the chrysalis. This causes its body to expand and split the case open. The butterfly crawls out and finds a place to hang while its wings expand and dry out before it is able to fly away.

CHRYSALIS

Once the caterpillar is fully grown, it finds a safe place to pupate, where it attaches itself to a stem or rests on the ground. Here, it sheds its skin to reveal a case known as a chrysalis. Inside this protective shell, its body breaks down and rearranges itself into its adult form.

ABOUT BUTTERFLY FAMILIES

BUTTERFLIES ARE GROUPED into six families according to the characteristics they share. For example, skippers are moth-like butterflies with clubbed antennae, which inhabit grasslands; fritillaries are medium to large butterflies with orange and brown wing patterns and caterpillars that feed on violets.

Knowing about the family groups helps you to identify butterflies out in the field and to understand more about their behaviour. Adult butterflies are generally doing one of the following: looking for a mate, defending their territory, feeding, basking in the sun or roosting. They all have their different styles of performing these basic life functions, and that is where knowing about the families really helps.

SWALLOWTAILS

Family: Papilionidae
These are large, colourful butterflies with swallow-like tails on their hindwings. The UK has only one of the 600 species that make up the swallowtail family.

SKIPPERS

Family: Hesperiidae
Named after their skipping flight, these are very moth-like butterflies. There are over 3,500 species worldwide and we have eight species in the UK.

WHITES & YELLOWS

Family: Pieridae
The clue is in the name, for these butterflies have white and/or yellow wings. There are about 1,100 species, some of which migrate each year in order to breed.

METALMARKS

Family: Riodinidae
The Duke of Burgundy is Europe's only metalmark, for most live in tropical regions. The name comes from the metallic wing markings of some species.

HAIRSTREAKS

Family: Lycaenidae
Hairstreaks, coppers and blues are small butterflies which belong to the Lycaenidae family. There are five hairstreaks and one copper species in the UK.

BLUES

Family: Lycaenidae
Although they are called blues, many of the females in this sub-family are brown. The UK has nine out of the 4,500 or so species of Lycaenidae worldwide.

VANESSIDS

Family: Nymphalidae
Vanessids, fritillaries and browns are part of the Nymphalidae family. The vanessids are the showy, colourful ones which bask in the sun with wings outstretched.

FRITILLARIES

Family: Nymphalidae
It is easy to recognise a fritillary by its orange and black wing patterns; it is harder to identify the actual species. Fritillary caterpillars often feed on the leaves of violets.

BROWNS

Family: Nymphalidae
About one-third of all butterflies in Europe are browns. They tend to inhabit grassy areas, where they fly close to the ground with a slow, jerky flight style.

FACTFILE

FOUND: Chalk & lime-
stone downlands
FLIES: May–June &
August–September
CATERPILLARS FEED ON:
Horseshoe vetch
WINGSPAN: 30–40 mm
FAMILY: Blues

ADONIS BLUE
Polyommatus bellargus

THE BLUE OF THE MALE Adonis blue butterfly is dazzling. It is easy to confuse with the common blue, but the colour of the Adonis blue is brighter and there are black lines running through its white wing edges. It lives in colonies on sunny hillsides in southern England, where it both feeds and lays its eggs on a yellow wild flower in the pea family called horseshoe vetch. It flies when the sun shines and often roosts in groups at night.

Records of this butterfly first start to appear in the United Kingdom (UK) in the early-18th century. It is named after the handsome youth Adonis in Greek mythology.

FEMALE BLUES
The family of blue butterflies is named after the males, for the uppersides of many female blues are brown. Yet if you look closely, you can see the females often have a light dusting of blue scales on their bodies, as on this female Adonis blue here.

ANTS
Like many blues, this butterfly has a special relationship with ants. The caterpillars have glands that produce honey-like substances, which ants feed on. This is good news for the caterpillars, as the ants protect them from predators such as wasps.

GRASS-EATING MAMMALS
The caterpillars of the Adonis blue eat only one thing – horseshoe vetch. This flower grows best where the grass is kept short by livestock or rabbits. If the number of either declines, so do horseshoe-vetch plants and the Adonis blues.

BLUES

THESE SMALL ACTIVE BUTTERFLIES belong to a family called Lycaenidae, along with coppers and hairstreaks. The term "blue" applies mostly to the males with blue uppersides, while the females are usually brown with a dusting of blue scales.

A CLOSER LOOK at a SILVER-STUDDED BLUE

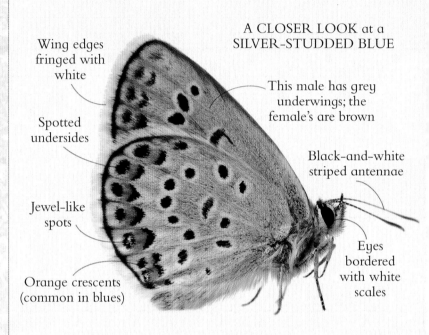

Wing edges fringed with white

Spotted undersides

Jewel-like spots

Orange crescents (common in blues)

This male has grey underwings; the female's are brown

Black-and-white striped antennae

Eyes bordered with white scales

EGGS

The eggs are disc-shaped with geometric patterns. Most are laid singly on plants in the pea family.

CATERPILLARS

The caterpillars have broad bodies with short hairs. Ants tend the caterpillars of many blue butterflies.

CHRYSALISES

The slug-like chrysalises are plain with rounded ends. They lie on the ground or form within ant nests.

BLUE BUTTERFLY GALLERY

Here are a few of the 80 European species of blue butterfly. Nine of these are resident in the UK – including the Adonis, common blue and silver-studded blue shown below.

MAZARINE BLUE

TURQUOISE BLUE

COMMON BLUE

It is the colour of the males that gives this family its name.

SILVER-STUDDED BLUE

ADONIS BLUE

GREEN-UNDERSIDE BLUE

The females are usually brown, with a light covering of blue scales.

SHORT-TAILED BLUE

GERANIUM BRONZE

LONG-TAILED BLUE

In some species, there is a short tail at the base of the hindwing.

BRIMSTONE
Gonepteryx rhamni

FEW BUTTERFLIES LIVE as long as the brimstone, which spends almost 12 months as an adult. The lemon-yellow males are woken from their winter sleep by the warmth of the sun. Fluttering along paths and hedgerows, they feed on flowers such as primroses and dandelions, in between searching for females.

By early summer, the previous year's brimstones have mated and laid their eggs. Their job is done. It is time for the new adults to emerge and feed themselves up before hibernating. Their long tongues are able to reach the sweet nectar stores of many flowers – often purple in colour – such as this scabious.

FROM EGG TO ADULT

The female brimstone seeks out the buds and tender new leaves of buckthorn trees in order to lay her bottle-shaped eggs. On hatching, the succulent leaves are eaten rapidly by the green caterpillars, which always lie concealed along the central vein (midrib) of the leaves. They will need some luck to avoid being eaten by birds such as this blue tit. Those that survive complete the next stage of their life as a leaf-shaped chrysalis before emerging two weeks later as a butter-coloured adult.

ROOSTING

Brimstones fly during the heat of the day. By mid-afternoon, they look for the underside of a leaf, such as this nettle, beneath which to roost. The leafy shape, colour and texture of their wings help them to hide in the foliage.

FACTFILE
FOUND: Hedgerows,
woodlands, scrub
FLIES: February–May
& August–September
CATERPILLARS FEED ON:
Species of buckthorn
WINGSPAN: 60–74 mm
FAMILY: Whites/Yellows

BROWN ARGUS
Aricia agestis

IN GREEK MYTHOLOGY, Argus was a giant with eyes all over his head, who was set to watch a nymph called Io. It didn't end well for Argus – he was slain – but his name lives on in a number of butterfly species with many eye-spots, like this one.

It may be surprising to learn that the brown argus is actually a type of blue butterfly. Despite the chocolate-brown upperwings of both males and females, they do behave like other blues: they fly close to the ground; they are sun-loving and territorial; they roost head-down at night and in poor weather; and they live in colonies in areas of chalk and limestone grasslands.

NORTHERN BROWN ARGUS

This is a close relation of the brown argus. In fact, it is almost identical, except that it is found further north and some individuals have white rather than black spots on their upperwings, as shown below on the right.

Both the northern brown and the brown argus butterflies spend the winter hibernating as caterpillars. When the weather is warm enough, the caterpillars become active again, transforming into chrysalises from which the adults emerge ready to mate and lay eggs.

ROCK-ROSES

Rock-roses are one of the few foodplants of brown and northern brown argus caterpillars. The caterpillars are hard to spot, but they do leave bare patches on rock-rose leaves where they have been feeding. Ants may also signal that the caterpillars are nearby.

FACTFILE

FOUND: Grasslands,
disturbed & fallow land

FLIES: April–June &
July–September

CATERPILLARS FEED ON:
Rock-rose, geranium

WINGSPAN: 25–31 mm

FAMILY: Blues

BROWNS

THESE SUMMER BUTTERFLIES belong to a family called Satyrinae, commonly called browns because of their colour. The eye-spots on their wings help to frighten away predators or lure them into attacking their wings and not other more important body parts.

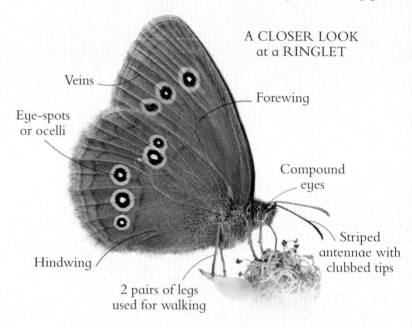

A CLOSER LOOK
at a RINGLET

Veins

Eye-spots
or ocelli

Forewing

Compound
eyes

Striped
antennae with
clubbed tips

Hindwing

2 pairs of legs
used for walking

EGGS

Females lay their dome-shaped eggs singly on the ground near to the caterpillars' foodplants.

CATERPILLARS

All caterpillars of the brown family feed on grasses. The caterpillars are brown or green and have short hairs.

CHRYSALISES

This chrysalis is lying on the ground, but some of this family's chrysalises hang from leaves, stems or stalks.

BROWN BUTTERFLY GALLERY

Europe has many satyrids or browns, some of which inhabit tiny geographical areas. We have 11 in the UK (marked below with a ★) and all bar the marbled white are brown in colour.

SMALL HEATH ★   SPECKLED   GATEKEEPER ★
WOOD ★

Some members of the brown family are among our commonest butterflies.

LATTICE BROWN   MARBLED   PEARLY HEATH
WHITE ★

The characteristic eye-spots are visible here on the wing undersides.

ARRAN BROWN   WALL ★   DRYAD

These browns are displaying the eye-spots on their wing uppersides.

BUTTERFLY HABITATS

A HABITAT IS AN AREA where a plant or animal lives. For some butterflies, the conditions of the habitat need to be just right. For example, caterpillars of the large blue butterfly feed on wild thyme found in well-drained grasslands – but only where a certain type of red ant lives. Other butterflies, such as red admirals, peacocks and small coppers, are less particular and can survive in a number of environments.

Many butterflies in danger of extinction can be saved by an understanding and management of the places where they live. Establishing wildlife corridors linking different habitats is important, too, in order to prevent individual butterfly colonies from becoming isolated or dying out.

GRASSLANDS

Butterflies inhabit three main types of grassland – chalk and limestone downlands; bracken-rich acid grasslands; and marshy grasslands. Many of these have been lost in recent years.

HEDGES & VERGES

These linking habitats provide a variety of food for adult butterflies and caterpillars. Look out for orange-tips in the spring, and for gatekeepers and meadow browns over the summer.

WOODLANDS

Woods are home to many butterflies such as the speckled wood, wood whites and some fritillaries. The best woodlands include mixed species with clearings and wide rides.

WETLANDS

The swallowtail is our only wetland species of butterfly. Its caterpillars feed on milk-parsley – a member of the carrot family, which grows in the watery fenlands and reedbeds of East Anglia.

MOUNTAINS & MOORLANDS

Few species of butterfly can survive the harsh climates of our uplands. The few that do include the large heath, Scotch argus and mountain ringlet, especially in sheltered grassy spots.

HEATHLANDS

Heaths are usually open, warm, dry, sandy places with low-growing shrubs such as heather, bracken and gorse. Heath fritillaries and small heaths are named after these habitats.

SCRUBLANDS & QUARRIES

Disused quarries, wasteland and railway banks with short, patchy vegetation are perfect habitats for dingy and grizzled skippers, as well as silver-studded blues and graylings.

PARKS & GARDENS

Many butterflies in parks and gardens stop to feed on nectar from flowers as they pass through. A few, such as red admirals and holly blues, use them to breed and hibernate in, too.

DUNES & CLIFFS

Warm, sandy soil and grass grazed by animals are a feature of many coastal areas. These make ideal conditions for butterflies such as walls, common blues and graylings.

CAMOUFLAGE

A BLUE TIT CHICK eats up to 100 caterpillars a day and there may be nine other chicks wanting food in just one nest. The parents need to find a lot of caterpillars!

A good way for a caterpillar to avoid being eaten is to avoid being seen. For this reason, many butterflies – at every stage of their life cycle – have colours, shapes and patterns that help them to blend into their backgrounds. The camouflage may be so spectacularly successful that it is almost impossible to see them.

This purple emperor chrysalis, for example, has the same oval shape, indentations and green colouring as the sallow tree leaf from which it hangs. It even has patterns on its surface that resemble the leaf's veins. Comma caterpillars and chrysalises take the leaf disguise further by having markings on their bodies that look like bird droppings.

CHALK HILL BLUE
Polyommatus coridon

THE BEST TIME TO SEE adult chalk hill blues is on sunny days between July and early September. No prizes for guessing where – chalk hillsides – and in a good year, there may be hundreds of males flying around in search of a female mate. The brown females are much harder to spot as they spend less time in flight, except when they are looking for food and laying eggs.

Blue is a rare colour in nature. Only one animal contains blue pigments, and that is the obrina olivewing butterfly. All the others – including this male chalk hill blue – appear to be blue only as a result of light waves reflecting off their wings.

FEMALE BLUES

Chalk hill blue females are brown with chequered wing fringes and have white edges to their black wing spots. You need to be quite skilled at butterfly identification in order to tell the difference between the similar females of the Adonis blue, common blue and chalk hill blue.

PUDDLING

Butterflies feed on the sugary nectar produced by flowers. Males also need salts and minerals to pass on to females when they mate. They obtain these from wet soil, rocks and animal faeces, as with these chalk hill blues sipping on some moist dung.

THE NOISY CHRYSALIS

Below is the slug-shaped chrysalis of the chalk hill blue. It is an unlikely musician, yet it produces squeaky sounds by rubbing rough segments of its outer case together. Scientists believe that this helps to attract ants, which then protect the chrysalis from predators.

FACTFILE
FOUND: Limestone
& chalk downland in
southern England
FLIES: July–September
CATERPILLARS FEED ON:
Horseshoe vetch
WINGSPAN: 33–40 mm
FAMILY: Blues

CLOUDED YELLOW

Colias croceus

THIS MAGNIFICENT GOLDEN BUTTERFLY is a summer visitor. It flies hundreds of miles from either north Africa or southern Europe, arriving in the UK from May onwards. Most years see a small influx, but once in a while thousands of them swarm across the channel, delighting butterfly-watchers.

Compared with the lemon-yellow of the male brimstone butterfly, the clouded yellow's colour is a much sunnier orange. It has thick black upperwing margins and noticeably pink legs, antennae and wing edges. Its flight is fast and powerful, and it pauses only briefly on a flower to feed before moving swiftly on.

RARE VISITORS

Very occasionally, two other clouded yellow species from mainland Europe find their way to the UK. These are Berger's clouded yellow (shown below) and the pale clouded yellow – and they are almost impossible to tell apart!

FEMALE CLOUDED YELLOWS

Below, a female clouded yellow is rejecting a male by raising her abdomen. She is one of the small number of female clouded yellows with creamy-coloured upperwings instead of golden-orange ones.

If the pair had mated, the female would have laid several hundred bottle-shaped eggs like these, which are white at first, changing to orange before hatching. They look huge in these photos, but they are only a millimetre long. They are laid on the leaves of plants in the pea family.

FACTFILE
FOUND: Woodland
rides & gardens
FLIES: February–May,
July & September
CATERPILLARS FEED ON:
Nettles, elms, hops
WINGSPAN: 50–64 mm
FAMILY: Vanessids

COMMA
Polygonia c-album

IF YOU SEE A BUTTERFLY on the wing on a sunny day in winter or spring, it will most likely be one that has hibernated as an adult. The comma is one of these, hiding itself among dead leaves in autumn, then awakening again in March. Each male sets up his own territory by picking a sunny spot from which to chase off unwelcome males or to intercept passing females.

The *polygonia* of the comma's scientific name refers to the many (*poly*) angles (*gon*) of its wing edges. No other UK butterfly has such indented wings; the degree varies between individuals, as does the intensity of the orange colouring.

THE COMMA

This butterfly is extremely difficult to spot when its wings are closed. There is just one mark that stands out against the dark background – the small, white "c" shape on its underwings, which gives this butterfly its name.

A BATTLE TO SURVIVE

The female comma lays her tiny ridged eggs on the leaves of nettles, currants, willows and hops, picking the plants with care. The caterpillars are armed for survival, with unappetising spikes on their bodies and markings that mimic bird droppings in order to fool predators. Each caterpillar sheds its skin as it grows, before finding a spot to turn into a chrysalis. This then hangs camouflaged to look like a dead leaf. Of the 250 eggs that can be laid, only a few will emerge as adults.

FACTFILE

FOUND: Where bird's-
foot-trefoil grows

FLIES: May–June &
July–October

CATERPILLARS FEED ON:
Trefoils, rest-harrows

WINGSPAN: 29–38 mm

FAMILY: Blues

COMMON BLUE

Polyommatus icarus

IF YOU SEE A FLASH OF BLUE darting between low-growing wild flowers in the summer, it could well be a male common blue. This butterfly is small, but this doesn't stop the male defending its territory fiercely, chasing away any butterflies that venture near. When not engaged in air wars, it seeks out a mate.

The upperwings of the females are largely brown, although this one on the left has more blue scales than many. The fact that the colours and markings of one species of butterfly can vary so much, combined with the similarity between species, is what makes butterfly identification so tricky.

SUBSPECIES

If you are in Ireland or north-west Scotland, you may be lucky enough to see the subspecies called *mariscolore*. The female (shown below) is larger and more blue than other common blues, and the orange markings are bolder.

ROOSTING

All butterflies roost at night and in wet weather when it is too cold or damp to fly. Common blues roost facing headdown on grasses. They are more vulnerable to attack like this, but their spots help to camouflage them.

FOODPLANTS

Clumps of common bird's-foot-trefoil light up grasslands in summer. Wherever it grows, you are likely to see common blues, like this male. The females lay their eggs singly on its leaves, which the caterpillars eat on hatching.

CONSERVATION

BUTTERFLIES ARE very sensitive to changes in their habitats. They are nature's fire alarms – alerting us to early problems in our finely balanced ecosystems. For some butterflies, any variation in the habitats on which they depend can be fatal, especially if the foodplants on which their caterpillars feed disappear.

The key factors that affect butterflies include loss of habitat, changes to the way land is used or managed, the effects of global warming and pollution, and the use of pesticides.

Butterfly Conservation and other wildlife organisations work hard to restore butterfly numbers and to reintroduce species, but the massive decline in insects in recent decades is a huge tide to turn. However, it IS possible to make a difference, as the reversal in fortunes of the large blue and the Duke of Burgundy has clearly shown.

COURTSHIP

As soon as a butterfly emerges as an adult, the clock is ticking for it to mate and produce the next generation. Males find females by sight or scent, either by actively seeking them out or by the less energy-demanding sit-and-wait approach.

Butterflies have scent organs on their bodies, which play a large part in courtship. These organs produce chemicals called pheromones, which help a butterfly to attract a mate. When the scent magic has worked, a male and female will lock together for anything between 10 minutes and five hours or more. The female will then search for a suitable place to lay her fertilised eggs.

Humans can also smell some of these scents. Those of the green-veined whites (shown here) have been described as lemony and those of the brown argus being like chocolate.

DARK GREEN FRITILLARY

Argynnis aglaja

PURPLE SEEMS TO BE a key colour for dark green fritillaries, for the adults feed on purple flowers such as thistles and knapweed and the female lays her eggs on the leaves of violets. The dark green in the name is due to the green sheen on the hindwings, visible when the wings are closed. Sage green fritillary might well have been a better name choice than dark green!

Look for these butterflies between July and August in rough grassy areas, dunes and woodland clearings. They roost at night in long grass, emerging to warm up in the early-morning sun before heading off to feed on nectar-filled flowers.

SPOT THE DIFFERENCE

The butterfly on the left is a dark green fritillary and the one on the right is a high brown fritillary. To the untrained eye, they look almost identical. However, if a butterfly in front of you looks a bit like either of these, it is most likely to be a dark green fritillary which commonly occurs throughout the UK. The high brown is extremely rare and is on the verge of extinction.

Dark green
fritillary

High brown
fritillary

VIOLETS

The caterpillars of a number of fritillary species feed on violets, including the black and red spiny caterpillars of the dark green fritillary. After hatching, its caterpillars immediately hibernate until the following spring.

FACTFILE

FOUND: Grasslands,
moorlands, scrub &
woodland clearings
FLIES: July–August
CATERPILLARS FEED ON:
Violets
WINGSPAN: 58–68 mm
FAMILY: Fritillaries

DAY-FLYING MOTHS

MOTHS BELONG TO THE SAME GROUP of insects as butterflies, called Lepidoptera, which means scaly wings. Unlike butterflies, most moths fly at night and are dull-coloured, which helps them to hide from predators while they rest.

However, there are some moths that are active during the day and can be easily mistaken for butterflies. Here are some of the most common day-flying moth species to look out for.

EMPEROR MOTH

This is a large moth. The male flies during the day in April and May. Look for its eye-spots and orange underwings.

NARROW-BORDERED BEE HAWK-MOTH

We have two hawk-moth species – narrow- and broad-bordered. Both hover as they sip nectar from flowers.

BURNET COMPANION

Burnet companions fly over grasslands from May to July, often in the company of other butterflies and moths.

CINNABAR

The red of these adult moths and their yellow-and-black caterpillars warn predators that they are poisonous if eaten.

GARDEN TIGER

By flashing its orange hindwings, this moth warns off predators. The hairy caterpillars are known as woolly bears.

SILVER Y

There is a bold "Y" on this moth's wings, hence its name. Large numbers of them migrate to the UK each year.

SIX-SPOT BURNET

Count the spots if you see a moth like this, for there are five- as well as six-spot species. This one is more widespread.

LATTICED HEATH

There are a number of chequered day-flying moths like this which fly both day and night in areas of grassland.

HUMMINGBIRD HAWK-MOTH

These fast flyers look like hummingbirds as they hover while they feed. Also, they make a humming noise in flight.

MOTHER SHIPTON

Mother Shipton was an 18th-century witch, and a hag-like face may be seen in the wing pattern of this grassland moth.

SPECKLED YELLOW

Looking down, you may see these yellow moths flying low in woodlands and scrubby areas in May and June.

CHIMNEY SWEEPER

The sooty black wings of the chimney sweeper moth are tipped with white. It flies in June and July in grassy meadows.

FORESTER

This green moth is found in damp meadows and marshes. It flies on sunny days and rests when it is overcast.

FOX MOTH

Only the male fox moth flies during the day. He is more red-brown than the greyer female and has feathery antennae.

JERSEY TIGER

Jersey tigers are exotic-looking large moths. They can be seen in gardens, woods and areas of waste ground.

DINGY SKIPPER

Erynnis tages

THERE ARE SOME BUTTERFLIES that are easy to recognise as they fly past, such as lemon-yellow brimstones in early spring. Not so the dingy skipper! Its flight is so rapid and its colours so muted that most people need a good view of it basking on bare earth before either noticing it or being able to identify it.

Dingy skippers are found in warm areas of short grassland throughout the UK, mostly in central and southern England. Like most species of butterfly, they have been in decline over recent decades because of changes in land use, but efforts to protect their habitat are helping to reverse this downward trend.

ROOSTING

While blue butterflies roost head downwards, dingy skippers roost head upwards. Unusually for butterflies, they rest on flowers or grasses with their hindwings tucked under their forewings in a triangular shape, as you can see here.

HIBERNATION

Females lay their eggs on flowers in the pea family. The caterpillars hatch out and go into hibernation once they are fully grown. It isn't until the following spring that they transform into chrysalises, emerging as adults a month later.

DINGY OR GRIZZLED?

With their hairy bodies and understated colours, the dingy and grizzled skippers are our most moth-like butterflies. You can tell the grizzled (below) from the dingy skipper by the bold white checks on its wings.

FACTFILE
FOUND: Waste ground, quarries & grasslands
FLIES: May–June & sometimes August
CATERPILLARS FEED ON: Pea-family plants
WINGSPAN: 27–34 mm
FAMILY: Skippers

DUKE OF BURGUNDY

Hamearis lucina

THIS RARE BUTTERFLY was in serious danger of dying out in the UK until conservation groups took action. Thanks to their efforts in the early-21st century, the lightly grazed grasslands and open woodland habitats of the Duke of Burgundy are on the increase. Importantly, this means that so too are the cowslips and primroses on which its caterpillars feed.

The Duke of Burgundy is a grand title for a butterfly that is a bit larger than a postage stamp. Its name is rather a mystery, but it is a definite rise in status from its first documented name – Mr Vernon's Small Fritillary – which appeared in the 17th century.

THE METALMARK FAMILY

The Duke of Burgundy looks like a fritillary, yet it belongs to the metalmark or Riodinidae family. It is the only one found in Europe – most of the 1,400 or so others live in South America. The name comes from the metallic markings of some species (not the Duke of Burgundy) like the punchinello, the double-banded Judy and the lesser harlequin shown below.

HINDWINGS

Below, you can see clearly two bands of white rectangles on the hindwing of the Duke of Burgundy. No other butterfly in the UK has markings like these and they are a sure sign that you are looking at a Duke of Burgundy.

Punchinello

Lesser harlequin

Double-banded Judy

46

FACTFILE

FOUND: Ancient
woods, limestone &
chalk grasslands
FLIES: May–June
CATERPILLARS FEED ON:
Cowslip, primrose
WINGSPAN: 29–34 mm
FAMILY: Metalmarks

FACTFILE

FOUND: Grasslands, verges, wood margins

FLIES: June–August

CATERPILLARS FEED ON: Mainly cock's-foot & creeping soft-grass

WINGSPAN: 26–30 mm

FAMILY: Skippers

ESSEX SKIPPER
Thymelicus lineola

THIS IS AN INSECT of flowery grasslands. The adults begin to appear in June, with males busily searching out females with which to mate. The range of the Essex skipper has been increasing over the years, unlike that of most butterflies, making it one of the winners of Earth's temperature warming up.

The females carefully select grasses with tightly furled leaves in which they lay their eggs in small rows. The caterpillars form inside the eggs – and then, guess what? They stay exactly like that, hidden away as eggs in their grassy world until the following spring when the caterpillars hatch out.

ANTENNAE
To distinguish between the very similar Essex and small skipper, look at the ends of their antennae. The Essex skipper's have black tips, while the small skipper's have orange undersides.

Essex skipper

Small skipper

NECTARING
The Duke of Burgundy (on the previous page) spends little time feeding, unlike Essex skippers. These small orange butterflies sip from flowers such as thistles, clovers, knapweeds and brambles in a process known as nectaring.

A GUIDE TO GRASSES
The female Essex skipper carefully selects a spot on a blade of grass on which to lay her eggs. Sometimes she chooses Timothy (left), but more frequently creeping soft-grass (middle) and cock's-foot (right).

FEEDING & POLLINATION

A BUTTERFLY does not need food to grow, it needs it for energy and for reproduction. Most of its food comes in the form of the sugary nectar produced by flowers, while other sources include sap from wounded trees and sweet liquid honeydew deposited on leaves by insects called aphids.

To suck these sweet liquids, the adult butterfly has a long feeding tube, or tongue, called a proboscis. You can see the small skippers here feeding – or nectaring, as it is known – on a thistle head. As they flit between flowers looking for nectar reserves, they carry pollen on their bodies, transferring it between male and female flower parts. This process is called pollination – and it is one on which we all depend, for it is only once a flower has been pollinated that fruit can form.

FRITILLARIES

FRITILLARIES BELONG to a large family of butterflies called Nymphalidae. Recognising a fritillary is reasonably easy – they all have orange-and-black checked markings. Trying to work out which one you are looking at can be very difficult, for the markings on different species may vary only slightly.

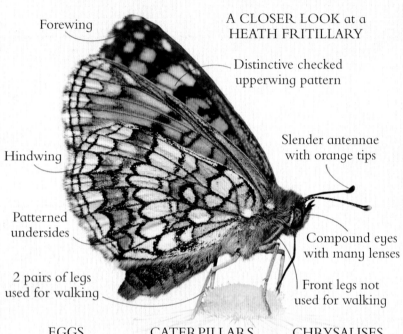

A CLOSER LOOK at a HEATH FRITILLARY

Forewing

Distinctive checked upperwing pattern

Slender antennae with orange tips

Hindwing

Patterned undersides

Compound eyes with many lenses

2 pairs of legs used for walking

Front legs not used for walking

EGGS

The eggs are barrel-shaped with vertical ridges. Some fritillaries lay eggs singly, others in clusters.

CATERPILLARS

Spikes like these are a feature of all fritillary caterpillars, even as they grow and shed their skin.

CHRYSALISES

A fritillary chrysalis usually hangs upside-down attached to a leaf or stem with a silken pad.

FRITILLARY BUTTERFLY GALLERY

Of the 100 species of fritillary worldwide, over 50 are found in Europe, with nine resident in the UK (those marked with a ★). The Glanville, high brown and heath fritillaries are rare.

HEATH FRITILLARY ★	GLANVILLE FRITILLARY ★	QUEEN OF SPAIN FRITILLARY

Fritillaries are instantly recognisable by their orange, brown and black markings.

WEAVER'S FRITILLARY	SPOTTED FRITILLARY	HIGH BROWN FRITILLARY ★

Fritillary undersides have varying patterns of orange, silver, black, white and brown.

SILVER-WASHED FRITILLARY ★	FALSE HEATH FRITILLARY	PEARL-BORDERED FRITILLARY ★

Checking the undersides of the wings really helps with identification.

GARDENING FOR BUTTERFLIES

COMMON GARDEN BUTTERFLIES include small tortoiseshells, red admirals and holly blues. It is easy to attract butterflies like these to your garden or balcony – all you need to do is to choose the right kinds of flower and plant them in warm, sheltered spots. Here are a few of the most nectar-rich species to grow – and there are many others that are popular with butterflies, too.

If you have space, try leaving an area for wild flowers. Some will establish themselves of their own accord, such as brambles, clover, thistles and dandelions, and you could try scattering some wild-flower seed mixes as well. These all provide vitally important sources of nectar for insects in general and may attract a range of butterflies to your garden.

AUBRIETA	PRIMROSE	HONESTY

This is a magnet for spring butterflies such as red admirals and orange-tips when there are few plants in flower.	Some adult butterflies fly in early spring on sunny days. Growing primroses provides them with the food they need.	Like aubrieta, this is a cabbage family member. It is popular especially with brimstones and orange-tips in spring.

BUDDLEIA

You need quite a large garden to grow this shrub. If you do, you will be rewarded with butterflies of all kinds.

LAVENDER

Plant lavender in a sunny, well-drained spot and spend the summer watching butterflies like this clouded yellow.

MARJORAM

A herb garden is great for attracting butterflies. Marjoram is popular with meadow browns and common blues.

SCABIOUS

Field and devil's-bit scabious are two late-flowering plants that provide nectar when other sources are over.

HEMP AGRIMONY

This tall, rather untidy-looking plant likes damp conditions and attracts silver-washed fritillaries and small coppers.

ASTER

Red admirals feed on the nectar from autumn-flowering plants such as asters, as well as the sugars from rotting fruit.

GARDENING FOR CATERPILLARS

THE PLANTS ON WHICH FEMALE butterflies choose to lay their eggs are known as host plants. For us, a host is someone who welcomes us as their guest. In the world of butterflies, a host plant is an unsuspecting victim, whose leaves have been chosen specially for their ability to give hungry caterpillars an endless supply of energy-giving meals.

If you want to encourage butterflies to your garden, try growing some of their caterpillars' host plants. Most butterflies will lay their eggs only on particular species of plant, with the ones shown here being among the most popular. Remember that females are very particular about the quality of the plants they select, and sheltered, sunny spots are preferable.

NASTURTIUMS	VETCHES	CRUCIFERS

Large and small whites feed on nasturtiums. This may help to stop them devouring nearby cabbage family plants.

Caterpillars of certain whites, skippers, blues and hairstreaks feed on plants in the vetch or pea family.

Crucifers such as garlic mustard, cuckooflowers and cabbages are popular with many white-family butterflies.

IVY

Ivy is an easy plant to grow and comes with the benefit of attracting holly blue butterflies to your garden.

BLACKTHORN

Blackthorn leaves are food for brown and black hairstreak caterpillars; they are good for moth caterpillars, too.

NETTLE

Peacocks, red admirals and commas lay their eggs on nettles, which provide enough food for all their caterpillars.

BUCKTHORNS

Purging and alder buckthorns are the sole foodplants of the brimstone. Young shrubs are preferred.

YORKSHIRE FOG

This grass forms tufts, which caterpillars of the marbled white and small skipper hide in when they are not feeding.

FESCUES

Brown butterflies and skippers often lay their eggs on grasses like this red fescue. Some feed by day, others by night.

FACTFILE

FOUND: Hedgerows &
open woodlands

FLIES: July–August

CATERPILLARS FEED ON:
Grasses such as bents,
fescues, meadow grass

WINGSPAN: 37–48 mm

FAMILY: Browns

GATEKEEPER
Pyronia tithonus

SOME YEARS, HEDGEROWS seem to be alive with clouds of gatekeepers nectaring on flowers such as bramble, water mint and wild thyme. Their tongues are quite short compared with those of many other butterflies, and so they feed on flatter flowers where the nectar reserves are not too deep.

In the summer, the female lays her eggs in long grass. The caterpillars hatch out and start to grow, moulting twice before hiding themselves away for the winter. In May, they continue to grow until the caterpillars are ready to pupate. The adults emerge in July and the process repeats itself.

TIPS FOR IDENTIFICATION

The male gatekeeper in the main picture has brown patches on his forewings, which the female (below) lacks. These are scales which release scents to attract females.

It is easy to confuse gatekeepers with meadow browns, for they look alike and fly at the same time and in similar habitats. The tiny white dots in the black circles on the forewings provide the key to identification. With wings closed, the meadow brown has one white spot, while the gatekeeper has two. The gatekeeper also has tiny white dots on its hindwings.

PREDATORS

Dragonflies, like this common hawker, are fearsome hunters which catch butterflies such as gatekeepers in mid-air. Spiders prey on the adults, too, while gatekeeper caterpillars may provide food for hungry birds.

Meadow brown

Gatekeeper

Female gatekeeper

59

GRAYLING
Hipparchia semele

ALTHOUGH THIS GRAYLING is settled on a flower, it isn't known for being an avid feeder and you are most likely to see one basking on some bare patch of earth or on a rock. The grayling thrives in dry uncultivated conditions and will tilt its wings towards the sun to help it warm up.

The brown family, to which the grayling belongs, share certain characteristics – being brown is obviously one of them, along with eye-like markings on their wings. These confuse predators into thinking that the butterflies are larger than they really are or that they are another, more fearsome animal entirely.

CAMOUFLAGE

This is the largest of the brown butterflies, but that doesn't make it any easier to spot. Its marbled grey-brown underside wing pattern helps it to blend in with the bare earth and rocks on which it basks.

LIFE CYCLE OF THE GRAYLING

The female grayling spends time selecting the ideal grass on which to lay her white-ribbed eggs. A caterpillar develops inside each one, nibbling a hole in the top of the egg when it is ready to emerge.

It starts its eating journey on nearby grasses and, like most butterflies, it hibernates as a caterpillar. Its development continues the following spring – when its foodplants start growing again – and by June it is ready to pupate. What happens next is unusual: it weaves a silky shroud in the earth, inside which the chrysalis lies. Four weeks later, it has transformed into an adult.

FACTFILE

FOUND: Coastland, dry grasslands & quarries

FLIES: July–September

CATERPILLARS FEED ON: Grasses such as hairgrasses & fescues

WINGSPAN: 51–62 mm

FAMILY: Browns

GREEN HAIRSTREAK

Callophrys rubi

APRIL IS THE MONTH when this, the first of our wonderful hairstreak butterflies, appears. It is unmistakable and magnificent and it is our only green butterfly. You are most likely to see it in patches of scrubland and hedgerows, especially if its brilliant green hindwings catch the sunlight – and your eye – as it perches on a leaf or takes nectar from a flower.

The four other hairstreaks found in the UK overwinter as eggs. However, the green hairstreak spends the time from August to the following May (about 10 months) as a brown, oval-shaped chrysalis before finally emerging as an adult.

BRAMBLE NAMES

The *rubi* part of the green hairstreak's scientific name means bramble. It was thought to feed exclusively on this plant, but it is now known to feed on many more. In German, it is called *Brombeerzipfelfalter* which means bramble hairstreak.

STRIDULATION

Sounds produced by animals moving hard body parts together is known as stridulation. Grasshoppers "sing" by rubbing ridges on their hindlegs against their forewings. The chrysalis of the green hairstreak makes clicks by grinding two sections of its outer case together, as do other butterflies such as the chalk hill blue.

The sound attracts nearby red ants, which then tend to the chrysalis, offering it some protection from predators. The ants may even drag it down into their nest, which keeps it further away from danger.

FACTFILE

FOUND: Any damp grassy habitat

FLIES: April–June & July–October

CATERPILLARS FEED ON: Crucifers

WINGSPAN: 40–42 mm

FAMILY: Whites/Yellows

GREEN-VEINED WHITE
Pieris napi

THIS IS ONE OF THE WORLD'S most successful butterfly species, found throughout Europe, North America, North Africa and parts of Asia. It appears early in the year – from late March onwards – in damp habitats, where the adults spend a lot of time feeding on flowers such buttercups, bugle and this watermint.

The green-veined white warms up in the morning by using its wings to direct the sun's rays onto its body until it has enough energy to fly. With its wings closed, the smudgy grey vein markings make it easy to identify, but with its wings open, it is easy to confuse with our large and small white butterflies.

CATERPILLAR FOODPLANTS

The caterpillars of the green-veined white feed only on wild cabbage species (crucifers) which include cuckooflower and garlic mustard (shown below). The green colour of the caterpillars camouflages them against the leaves on which they feed.

A TALE OF TWO BROODS

There are at least two, occasionally three, generations of green-veined white a year, with the adults of each brood having slightly different wing patterns, as shown below. This is described as seasonal variation.

Spring: the markings on the underwings are quite dark. The female has two spots on her upperwings, while the male's are almost white.

Summer: the butterflies are bigger and more numerous. The underwing markings are paler and the male now has one spot on his upperwings.

Spring brood

Summer brood

GRIZZLED SKIPPER
Pyrgus malvae

THE ADULT GRIZZLED SKIPPERS emerge in April and the male soon sets up his territory. He swoops on any intruding butterfly and will engage in some spectacular aerial chases to maintain his position. When the females arrive, he releases some potent scents from his wings, which he hopes will be impossible to resist.

It is the erratic, jumpy flight patterns of skippers that give this family its name. Skippers are fast fliers; some species reach speeds of up to 37 miles an hour, powered by muscles in their thick bodies. This speed and manoeuvrability help them to avoid predators – but not all, as you can see in the panel below.

ROOSTING
From late afternoon and in poor weather, the grizzled skipper rests on dead flowerheads and grasses. The dappled markings of its underwings help to camouflage it.

EGG-LAYING
If you are walking in a sunny wood or on a chalky down in June, you may see a female grizzled skipper looking for a place to lay her bun-shaped eggs. Low-growing plants in the rose family are favoured, especially near bare patches of earth.

PREDATORS
A robberfly will trap and eat anything it can catch, including butterflies such as the grizzled skipper. Its prey caught, it uses its beak to inject poison into its prey. This kills and breaks down its victim's insides, which it then drinks as a soup.

FACTFILE

FOUND: Waste ground,
chalk downlands &
woodland rides

FLIES: April–June

CATERPILLARS FEED ON:
Wild strawberry

WINGSPAN: 52–62 mm

FAMILY: Skippers

HAIRSTREAKS

THESE SMALL BUTTERFLIES belong to the same Lycaenidae family as coppers and blues. They are not generally wellknown, for they are less showy than some of our common butterflies and are frequently out of sight, perched in trees or bushes.

A CLOSER LOOK at a
BROWN HAIRSTREAK

Female brown hairstreaks have bold markings on their upperwings

Thin white lines, or streaks, on the underwings

Wavy edges to hindwings

Striped antennae with orange tips

Black eyes bordered with white scales

Short tail

3 pairs of legs used for walking

EGGS

CATERPILLARS

CHRYSALISES

The bun-shaped eggs are laid singly or in twos or threes and are covered in geometric patterns.

The segmented caterpillars shed their skin four times until they are fully grown and ready to pupate.

Most hairstreak chrysalises lie on or near the ground like this or are attached to stems, leaves or twigs.

HAIRSTREAK BUTTERFLY GALLERY

Many European hairstreaks look remarkably similar. To identify them, you need to be familiar with the fine underwing markings, or hairstreaks, which give these butterflies their name.

PURPLE HAIRSTREAK

BROWN HAIRSTREAK

Hairstreaks keep their wings firmly together except for purple and brown hairstreaks.

BLACK HAIRSTREAK

GREEN HAIRSTREAK

WHITE-LETTER HAIRSTREAK

The butterflies shown above are the five hairstreaks resident in the UK.

BLUE-SPOT HAIRSTREAK

PROVENÇAL HAIRSTREAK

ILEX HAIRSTREAK

A further 10 species, including these ones, can be found in mainland Europe.

FACTFILE

FOUND: Gardens, woodlands, hedgerows

FLIES: April–May & July–August

CATERPILLARS FEED ON: Mainly holly & ivy buds

WINGSPAN: 26–34 mm

FAMILY: Blues

HOLLY BLUE
Celastrina argiolus

HOW DO YOU KNOW if you are looking at a holly blue? It almost certainly is one if: it is April or early May; it is flying or perched around head-height or above; and its underwings are pure sky blue with tiny spots. Our other blue butterflies first appear slightly later in the year, fly closer to the ground and have different markings on their underwings.

Spring sees this small butterfly lay its eggs at the base of holly flower buds. Two weeks later, tiny caterpillars hatch out and devour the surrounding leaves and flowers. Holly blues have a second brood in autumn – this time they lay their eggs on ivy.

PARASITES
Populations of holly blues can be devastated by parasitic wasps. One species (*Listrodromus nycthemerus*) lays its eggs only in the caterpillars of holly blues. Its grubs feed on the developing caterpillars until just one wasp emerges from each chrysalis (below).

PUDDLING
Holly blues feed on nectar and honeydew – a sweet substance deposited on plants by insects called aphids. The males also need minerals and salts to pass on to females when mating. They sip these from the ground in an activity called puddling.

FOODPLANTS
These are one of our most common garden visitors. The best way to encourage them to visit yours is to plant holly and ivy on which they lay their eggs, along with gorse, spindle, dogwoods and bramble on which the adults feed.

71

LARGE BLUE
Phengaris arion

THE LARGE BLUE IS ONE of our rarest butterflies. It is found only on closely cropped grasslands where wild thyme grows and the red ant (*Myrmica sabuleti*) lives. So particular are its needs that it became extinct in the UK in 1979. Since then, conservation programmes have reintroduced individuals brought from Sweden to carefully managed sites where their numbers are increasing.

The adults fly from late May to early July and live on average for a mere five days. You are most likely to see them in the morning or late afternoon in good weather, when males are out patrolling their territory in search of females with which to mate.

THE CATERPILLAR'S STORY

An egg (this one is magnified) is laid on a flower bud and a caterpillar hatches out. Its diet includes wild thyme and other large blue caterpillars! Three weeks later it falls to the ground, where it is found by ants. They caress the caterpillar with their feelers, stimulating it to produce a sweet substance on which they feed. Then the caterpillar rears up, pretending to be a lost ant grub, and the unsuspecting ants carry it back to their nest.

For 10 months, the caterpillar grows by feeding on ant grubs until it transforms into a chrysalis – still tended to by the ants. Three weeks pass before the adult emerges, crawls out of the ant nest, and flies off.

LARGE BLUE MARKINGS

You can tell you are looking at a large blue butterfly if you see black spots on its upperwings, for no other blue butterfly in the UK has them. The female – shown below – is larger than the male and has darker markings on its upperwings.

FACTFILE

FOUND: Peat bogs & damp moorlands

FLIES: June–August

CATERPILLARS FEED ON: Hair's-tail cottongrass

WINGSPAN: 35–42 mm

FAMILY: Browns

LARGE HEATH

Coenonympha tullia

THIS TAWNY BROWN BUTTERFLY inhabits damp moorlands and peat bogs in some of the UK's remotest areas. Its caterpillars eat hare's-tail cottongrass, and conditions have to be just right for this to grow. There also need to be supplies of a type of heather called cross-leaved heath, on which the adults feed.

The large heath may be seen flying between late June and August often in cloudy conditions which many other butterflies avoid. It lives in colonies, at times in their thousands, and rarely ventures far from its immediate surroundings. The upperwings are only visible in flight as it always rests with its wings closed.

SUBSPECIES

The number of spots on the large heath varies considerably between individuals in the same area and also from region to region. In the north of Scotland, there is a subspecies known as *scotia* (shown below) with barely any spots.

PREDATORS

The large heath may face a number of predators in the course of its life cycle. Birds, such as this meadow pipit, prey on the adults in flight, and parasitic wasps inject their eggs into large heath caterpillars, on which their grubs then feed.

PEAT BOGS

Peat bogs are wetlands made up of decaying plant material. Careful management of this habitat is crucial for the large heath's survival. Its numbers declined seriously last century when changes to the peat bogs led to loss of its foodplant.

LARGE SKIPPER
Ochlodes sylvanus

YOU MAY CATCH SIGHT of this burnt-orange butterfly in gardens, flitting between flowers into which it dips its long tongue in search of nectar. Unlike some of the bigger butterflies which glide along breezily, skippers are stockier and fly with purpose. Theirs is a perch-and-pursue policy towards passing females, while they aggressively chase away butterfly intruders.

The term "large" in this butterfly's name is slightly misleading, for it is about the size of a grape and only slightly bigger than the small skipper. It holds its wings in a compact "V" shape, which has the effect of reducing its apparent size further.

CHEQUERED SKIPPER

This is the rarest member of the skipper family. It flies between May and June but only in a few small regions of Scotland where the purple moor-grass grows on which its caterpillars feed.

The chequered skipper became extinct in England in the mid-1970s as the woods in which it bred became too overgrown and shady. However, in 2018 it was re-introduced, and through careful habitat management it is hoped that its numbers will increase.

MARKINGS

The male large skipper has a dark line on its forewings made up of scales which release scents to attract females. The undersides of both sexes have faint spots, which the small and Essex skippers lack.

FACTFILE
FOUND: Grasslands,
wood clearings, hedges
FLIES: June–August
CATERPILLARS FEED ON:
Cock's-foot & other
coarse grasses
WINGSPAN: 29–36 mm
FAMILY: Skippers

LARGE WHITE
Pieris brassicae

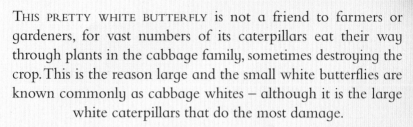

THIS PRETTY WHITE BUTTERFLY is not a friend to farmers or gardeners, for vast numbers of its caterpillars eat their way through plants in the cabbage family, sometimes destroying the crop. This is the reason large and the small white butterflies are known commonly as cabbage whites – although it is the large white caterpillars that do the most damage.

Some butterflies live in colonies and stay rooted to the area. Not so the large white. Every year, huge numbers of these powerful flyers migrate from northern Europe, with some arriving in the UK to join the resident population.

PREDATORS

Much research has gone into finding animals that prey on large white caterpillars, because of the destruction they cause. They do have many predators including parasitic wasps, ground beetles (below) and viruses, but not enough to keep large white numbers in check.

CATERPILLARS

Most butterflies lay their eggs singly on plants, but large whites lay clusters of between 40 and 100 yellow eggs at a time. Once hatched, the caterpillars move in bands, leaving a trail of shredded vegetables in their wake.

MARKINGS

Dot, dot, dash (think Morse code) go the spots on the female's upperwings, while the male has none. Both sexes have black crescent tips to their wings. Those of the small white are similar but do not extend as far down.

FACTFILE

FOUND: Scrubby areas
& flowery grasslands

FLIES: June–August

CATERPILLARS FEED ON:
Grasses such as fescues,
& Yorkshire-fog

WINGSPAN: 53–58 mm

FAMILY: Browns

MARBLED WHITE
Melanargia galathea

THE BOLD MARKINGS of the marbled white butterfly signal to predators that it is poisonous and should be avoided. It gets the toxins in its body from a fungus that is found in the grasses on which its caterpillars feed. The big surprise about this butterfly is that despite its colouring it is a member of the brown family.

Its peak flight time is in July, but the marbled white may be spotted on flowery grasslands any time between June and August. Once it has warmed up in the morning sun, it spends much of the day nectaring on purple flowers such as wild marjoram, thistles and knapweed and at night it roosts headdown on grasses.

OTHER SPECIES

Some butterflies vary considerably between individuals and from region to region, but not the marbled white. In the south of Europe, there are seven other marbled white species, all with slightly different markings, such as this Balkan marbled white.

FROM EGG TO CHRYSALIS

The story begins when the female scatters her eggs on the ground. There is no careful choosing of tender leaves on which to place her eggs as is the case with most butterflies. On hatching, the caterpillars soon enter hibernation. The following spring, they wake up, start to eat and grow until they are ready to pupate. It takes up to 25 days for the chrysalis to transform into an adult.

You can see the black and white pattern of the butterfly's wings through the shell of the chrysalis below. The case is about to split and the adult butterfly emerge – one of the few that will reach the final stage of development.

MARSH FRITILLARY

Euphydryas aurinia

THE ODDS ARE STACKED against the survival of the marsh fritillary: several parasitic wasp species use the butterfly as their host, wiping out huge numbers in some years. Also, the grassland areas it inhabits require careful management to keep the grasses at just the right height for the butterfly's foodplants to flourish.

In the tricky world of fritillary identification, this one is more easily recognisable than some others. In most individuals, its upperwings are more colourful than those of other fritillaries. It also has tiny yellow spots in the orange band on its forewings and equally small black ones on the orange band on its hindwings.

GLANVILLE FRITILLARY

This is another butterfly that needs protecting, for it is found only on the Isle of Wight in the UK. It flies between May and July on warm grassy sites and its caterpillars feed on ribwort plantain.

DEVIL'S-BIT SCABIOUS

The female marsh fritillary chooses where to lay her eggs with care. Only the lushest, largest leaves of the devil's-bit scabious (below) will do. She is right to be picky, for the plant needs to feed lots of caterpillars.

EGG CLUMPS

This is one of nine UK species to lay its eggs in clumps instead of singly. The female may carry several hundred before depositing them, which makes flying difficult. The eggs are yellow at first before turning red and then grey.

FACTFILE
FOUND: Damp or
chalk grasslands &
moorlands
FLIES: May–July
CATERPILLARS FEED ON:
Devil's-bit scabious
WINGSPAN: 30–50 mm
FAMILY: Fritillaries

FACTFILE
FOUND: Wide variety
of grasslands
FLIES: May–September
CATERPILLARS FEED ON:
Grasses such as bents
& fescues
WINGSPAN: 40–60 mm
FAMILY: Browns

MEADOW BROWN
Maniola jurtina

AT THE HEIGHT OF SUMMER, you may come across bushes seemingly alive with meadow browns. They are one of our commonest butterflies, found throughout Europe in almost any area of grassland where they fly in all but the heat of the day.

The male (left) is smaller than the female. His wings were once a rich brown but they have started to fade. This happens to all butterflies as they lose the scales from their wings. It isn't flying long distances that causes this, but the daily wear and tear of feeding and mating. The dark brown smudges you can see are scent glands, which release chemicals to attract females.

FEMALES

Compare the markings of the female below with the male's on the left. The amber patches on her upperwings are similar to those of the male gatekeeper. However, she has one white dot in the eye-spots on her forewings, while the gatekeeper has two.

NECTARING

A meadow brown will spend much of the day nectaring at many kinds of flowers, such as the field scabious below. Its long feeding tube – known as a proboscis – dips into each flower, searching for the sugary nectar reserves, which it then drinks up.

CATERPILLARS

The female lays her eggs in grassy areas. The tiny caterpillars that hatch out are brown at first and soon become bright green, camouflaging them well amongst the vegetation. They hibernate as caterpillars, awakening in spring to continue their growth.

MIGRATION

WHY WOULD YOU fly thousands of miles when your life span is short and you could stay put? The short answer is to find food, to escape difficult weather conditions and to avoid predators. These monarchs are among the world's greatest long-distance travellers, flying thousands of miles to improve their chances of survival.

Not all butterflies that migrate undertake massive journeys. Every year, our resident butterflies are joined by ones from Europe, such as clouded yellows and red admirals. The number may vary from a few hundred to millions, depending on the weather conditions and the food sources along the way. Unlike most other migratory animals, no one butterfly makes the full journey. Adults reproduce and die either along the migration route or on reaching their breeding grounds, leaving the next generation to continue the trip.

ORANGE-TIP

Anthocharis cardamines

IT IS THE MALE that gives this butterfly its name, for the female does not have the flashy orange tips to her wings. Her more modest white and black upperwings are very similar to those of the small white. However, she needs only to reveal her patterned undersides for there to be no doubt she is an orange-tip.

These are true springtime butterflies, emerging from their winter chrysalis state with the first prolonged sunshine of the year. The male appears first, in order to have the best chance of finding a freshly emerged female. He begins his mission to find a mate, erratically dipping into grassy sites hoping to seek one out.

CAMOUFLAGE

Camouflage is the best defence for many butterflies. For the orange-tip, its mottled greeny yellow underwings help to camouflage it against the plants on which it rests in the dappled light of the damp places it inhabits.

EGGS

It is a thrill to find the bottle-shaped eggs of the orange-tip, which are easier to spot than those of other butterflies. Look for them on flower stalks of garlic mustard and cuckooflower, or watch where females land and scour the plants afterwards.

CHRYSALISES

An adult male orange-tip is about to emerge from the chrysalis below. It has spent the winter in this form, spectacularly mimicking the seedpod of the plant to which it is attached. It is held in place by a silken thread around its middle and a silk pad at its base.

FACTFILE
FOUND: Any damp
grassy areas
FLIES: April–June
CATERPILLARS FEED ON:
Garlic mustard,
cuckooflower
WINGSPAN: 40–52 mm
FAMILY: Whites/Yellows

PAINTED LADY
Vanessa cardui

THIS IS THE MOST WIDESPREAD butterfly in the world – found on almost every continent except South America and Antarctica. It is a frequent visitor to the UK, flying any time from late spring to early autumn. You may see it feeding or with its salmon-pink wings outstretched basking on patches of earth to warm up.

The curled-up proboscis – visible on the right – unwinds to form a long feeding tube which reaches down to plunder the nectar sources of many different flowers. The caterpillars are more choosy, preferring plants in the thistle family. In fact, in many languages the painted lady is called the thistle butterfly.

AN INCREDIBLE JOURNEY

The migration of the painted lady is one of the wonders of the animal kingdom. It travels from central Africa to northern Europe and back in a year, flying about 8,000 miles. Unlike other butterflies, it does not hibernate. Instead, it reproduces at points along its route and may take up to eight generations to complete the round trip.

The journey requires a lot of energy and is hazardous – the weather may be bad, and sources of food along the way may prove difficult to find. As a result, some years see millions of painted ladies reaching our shores, while in other years there may be just a few hundred.

PREDATORS

This poor butterfly is enmeshed in the sticky silken web of a spider. Once it is caught, the spider rushes out to spin more threads around its helpless victim. Other animals that prey on painted ladies include parasitic wasps and birds such as flycatchers.

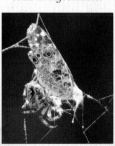

FACTFILE

FOUND: Open, dry
habitats

FLIES: May–June &
July–October

CATERPILLARS FEED ON:
Mainly thistles

WINGSPAN: 58–74 mm

FAMILY: Vanessids

FACTFILE
FOUND: Gardens, fields
& hedgerows
FLIES: February–May
& July–September
CATERPILLARS FEED ON:
Nettles
WINGSPAN: 63–74 mm
FAMILY: Vanessids

PEACOCK

Inachis io

WITH THE FIRST WARM SUN of the year, peacock butterflies come out of hibernation in search of nectar from spring flowers. After mating, the females lay hundreds of eggs in patches of nettles large enough to feed all the emerging caterpillars. These spiky larvae protect themselves from attack by weaving silken tents within which to hide and feed until they are ready to pupate.

Many in the vanessid family, to which the peacock belongs, have scientific names relating to Greek and Roman mythological characters. In this case, Io was a beautiful nymph loved by Zeus – king of the Greek gods – and Inachis was her father.

UNDERWINGS

Now you see me, now you don't. This is the effect the peacock gives with its wings open and then closed. The near-black undersides camouflage it against dark surfaces, especially when it is hibernating in old buildings and trees.

FORMS OF DEFENCE

Eye-spots form part of the wing patterns of many butterflies and some moths, too. Those on the hindwings of the eyed hawk-moth below are similar to those of the peacock (inset). Both insects flash their "eyes" at predators to convince them that they are larger creatures, while the spots on their wings help to deflect attack away from their vital organs.

The peacock can also rub its wings together to create a hissing sound which, when combined with flashing eye-spots, is enough to deter most would-be aggressors.

Eyed hawk-moth

FACTFILE
FOUND: Deciduous,
usually oak woodland
FLIES: July–August
CATERPILLARS FEED ON:
Mostly goat but also
grey and crack willow
WINGSPAN: 75–84 mm
FAMILY: Vanessids

PURPLE EMPEROR
Apatura iris

THIS IS OUR LARGEST BUTTERFLY after the swallowtail, yet it is one of the hardest to see. Not because it is near extinction, but because it spends its short life among the treetops in areas of oak woodland in southern England. It feeds on honeydew and tree sap instead of descending to ground level to take nectar from flowers – which is another reason it is so hard to spot.

Between July and August, the newly emerged males establish their territories on prominent trees where they perch waiting for passing females. It is only the male that has the purple sheen to its wings; the female's wings are largely brown.

FEEDING

The best time to spot these striking butterflies is mid-morning. This is when male purple emperors may descend to feed on the three "d"s – dead animals, damp ground and dung. These provide nutrients which they pass on to females when they mate.

CATERPILLARS

The purple emperor spends 300 days as a caterpillar, from August until the following June. If you should be lucky enough to find one, identification is relatively easy. Look for two horns on its head, which become visible after the first moult.

FEMALES

Camouflaged against tree trunks and branches, the brown and white female is harder to spot than the male. One of the only times she descends from the canopy is to lay her beautiful conical eggs on the upper side of willow leaves.

PURPLE HAIRSTREAK

Neozephyrus quercus

HOW MANY BUTTERFLIES can you name? The purple hairstreak is unlikely to be one of them. However, it is the most common of the hairstreaks and is found widely throughout Europe. It spends little time in flight except on sunny days in late afternoon, when many other butterflies have gone to roost.

Most hairstreaks rest with their wings tightly closed but the purple hairstreak basks and feeds with them open. This affords a good view of the upperwings: the male's are covered in a purple sheen which in certain lights looks black; and the female's (in the main picture) are dark brown with smart violet patches.

TREE LIFE

These small butterflies spend most of their adult lives in the canopy of sheltered oak trees. Males gather on leaves in sunny spots waiting for passing females. They rarely feed from flowers, preferring sweet honeydew deposits left by aphids.

MARKINGS

With their wings closed, most hairstreaks look alike, with browny-grey colouring and fine white lines. However, the purple hairstreak is the only one to have an orange and black eye-spot at the base of each hindwing – a helpful defining feature!

FINDING EGGS

Try looking for the tiny, white, bun-shaped eggs of the purple hairstreak at the base of oak-tree buds in winter. The female lays her eggs in ones or twos in summer, and it isn't until the following spring that the caterpillars hatch out – just as the buds open.

FACTFILE
FOUND: Sunny glades
and woodland edges
with oak trees
FLIES: July–August
CATERPILLARS FEED ON:
Oak leaves
WINGSPAN: 33–38 mm
FAMILY: Hairstreaks

RECORDING BUTTERFLIES

THE NATURAL WORLD is in crisis. Our insect populations have plummeted, and many of our butterfly species are declining so rapidly that they are in danger of disappearing from certain areas altogether. What can we do to help? A surprising amount, as it happens.

Simply by recording the butterflies around you and sharing your findings with scientists, you can help them to develop ways to save our most threatened species.

The best way to start is by taking part in Butterfly Conservation's Big Butterfly Count, held annually in July and August, which involves recording the butterflies in your garden for 15 minutes. If you want to do more, there are other national schemes which involve regular monitoring of a local area. For more information, go to www.butterfly-conservation.org.

RED ADMIRAL
Vanessa atalanta

THE COLOURS OF THIS HANDSOME butterfly resemble a smart uniform, which makes the word admiral easy to remember. Every spring, the few adults that manage to survive the winter here are joined by large numbers migrating from southern Europe and north Africa. They reproduce and die on the journey, taking three or four generations to reach their final destination.

The undersides of the red admiral are rather mix-and-match, with brightly coloured forewings and mottled brown hindwings. To hide itself from predators, it often rests with just the cryptically coloured hindwings showing.

ATTRACTING RED ADMIRALS

If you have flown or are about to fly over 2,000 miles, you desperately need food. Growing nectar-rich plants such as buddleia (shown below) is a great way to entice red admirals into your garden. They also feed on the sugars produced by rotting fruit which you can leave out for them if there are no fruit trees nearby.

The hungry caterpillars feed on young nettle leaves, which are not difficult to grow. Make sure that your nettle patch is in a sunny, sheltered position for the best chance of encouraging females to lay their eggs there.

CHRYSALIS

In a tent of folded leaves hangs the chrysalis. Its green chamber is created by the caterpillar before it pupates, in order to hide from predators. If you see a group of nettle leaves spun together, you may find a chrysalis.

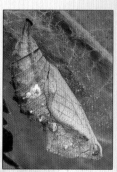

FACTFILE

FOUND: Gardens, orchards, parks and other flowery habitats

FLIES: June–October

CATERPILLARS FEED ON: Nettles

WINGSPAN: 64–78 mm

FAMILY: Vanessids

FACTFILE
FOUND: Sheltered,
damp, grassy places
FLIES: June–August
CATERPILLARS FEED ON:
Grasses such as cock's–
foot & couch grass
WINGSPAN: 42–52 mm
FAMILY: Browns

RINGLET
Aphantopus hyperantus

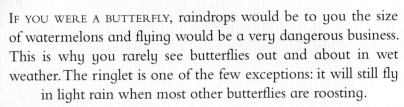

IF YOU WERE A BUTTERFLY, raindrops would be to you the size of watermelons and flying would be a very dangerous business. This is why you rarely see butterflies out and about in wet weather. The ringlet is one of the few exceptions: it will still fly in light rain when most other butterflies are roosting.

The ringlet's favoured habitat is damp, tussocky grassland where there is protection from the wind and the air is reasonably humid. The male on the left is basking in the morning sun, warming up its flight muscles before heading off in search of females or to sip nectar from nearby brambles or thistles.

MARKINGS

This butterfly does eye-spots supremely well. The golden rings on its wing undersides – with their black and white inner circles – identify it immediately as a ringlet. Note that the size and shape of the eye-spots may vary.

MOUNTAIN RINGLET

This is not a butterfly that you are likely to stumble upon unless you live in or are passing through any of Europe's mountain ranges, including the Lake District and the Scottish Highlands. Even there, it is hard to spot.

Mountain ringlets have a short flight window between June and July, with adults living for just a few days. They are active on sunny days and may be seen flying low around grassy mountain slopes. They feed on wild flowers such as heath bedstraw and tormentil.

SCOTCH ARGUS
Erebia aethiops

UNLIKE THE RINGLET, the Scotch argus needs sunny weather. The sun's rays keep its flight muscles warm and help it to detect its surroundings, for its eyesight isn't as keen as that of many other butterflies. It lives in colonies in damp, sheltered grasslands in Scotland and a few sites in northern England, where it flies from late July through to early September.

Erebia in this butterfly's scientific name comes from the ancient Greek word "erebus" meaning shade or darkness, referring to its brown colour. There are 44 other similar-looking brown butterflies in Europe that belong to this same genus or group.

LIFE CYCLE

Most of this butterfly's life is spent out of sight among grassy mounds. The female lays her tiny eggs on sunny days in August, with the caterpillars hatching out two weeks later. They hibernate in this state before waking in spring to continue their life cycle.

This chrysalis (below right) is almost fully developed: you can just see the pattern of the adult's wings through the hard brown case. It won't be long before the butterfly emerges, waits for its wings to dry and flies away.

WING DAMAGE

The scales on butterfly wings fall off or fade as a butterfly ages, leaving some adults looking quite ragged, such as the Scotch argus below. The wings cannot regrow, but the butterfly can still fly if there is enough wing left.

SILVER-WASHED FRITILLARY

Argynnis paphia

LARGE, POINTED, ORANGE WINGS and a graceful, swooping flight style make this one of our most showy butterflies. Groups congregate to feed along wide woodland paths edged with patches of bramble, hemp agrimony and thistle. They are more approachable than most butterflies, giving onlookers a proper chance to appreciate their splendour.

Not only is this our largest fritillary species, it is also the only one to have the silvery-green sheen to its underwings. It is spreading northwards because of climate change and is now found across much of England and Wales.

COLOUR VARIATIONS

A small number of females in certain regions have an almost otherwordly purple-olive sheen to their wings, like this one. The form is called *valesina*, commonly referred to as the greenish-silver-washed fritillary.

COURTSHIP

A male will approach anything orange in the hope that it is a female. If he finds one, he tries to impress her by flying in a loop-the-loop around her, while showering her with scents called pheromones. These are released from the four brown bars across his upperwings (see below).

VIOLETS

The female is very particular about where she lays her eggs. First she finds the perfect patch of violets. Then she climbs up a nearby tree and lays her eggs in crevices in the bark. The following spring, the caterpillars make their way down to the forest floor where the violet feeding frenzy begins.

FACTFILE

FOUND: Woodland
rides, hedgerows
FLIES: June–August
CATERPILLARS FEED ON:
Violets, especially
common dog-violet
WINGSPAN: 69–80 mm
FAMILY: Fritillaries

SKIPPERS

THE SCIENTIFIC NAME of the skipper family is Hesperiidae. These are small, very moth-like butterflies and what they lack in size, they make up for in speed and manoeuvrability. Most have one generation a year and hibernate as either caterpillars or eggs.

A CLOSER LOOK at a
SILVER-SPOTTED SKIPPER

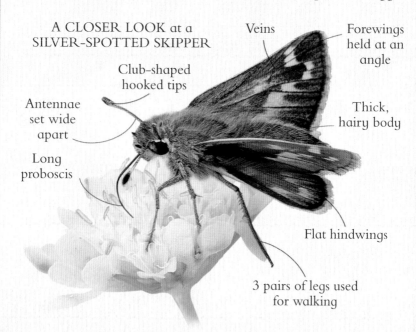

Veins

Forewings
held at an
angle

Club–shaped
hooked tips

Antennae
set wide
apart

Thick,
hairy body

Long
proboscis

Flat hindwings

3 pairs of legs used
for walking

EGGS

The eggs of butterflies in the skipper family may be laid singly or in small clusters on grasses.

CATERPILLARS

Skipper caterpillars often bind grass and other leaves together to form tubes inside which they hide.

CHRYSALISES

Chrysalises lie within a tent spun from leaves, or at the base of their foodplant in a silky case called a cocoon.

SKIPPER BUTTERFLY GALLERY

In Europe, there are over 40 species of skipper, most of which are either dark or golden in colour. Only eight of them are resident in the UK (all bar the olive and mallow skipper below).

DINGY SKIPPER

LULWORTH SKIPPER

OLIVE SKIPPER

These moth-like butterflies have thick, hairy bodies and large eyes.

LARGE SKIPPER

SMALL SKIPPER

ESSEX SKIPPER

These plus the Lulworth and silver-spotted species make up our golden skippers.

GRIZZLED SKIPPER

CHEQUERED SKIPPER

MALLOW SKIPPER

These spread-wing skippers rest with their wings outstretched.

FACTFILE

FOUND: Dunes & dry
grasslands

FLIES: May–June &
August–September

CATERPILLARS FEED ON:
Kidney vetch

WINGSPAN: 18–27 mm

FAMILY: Blues

SMALL BLUE
Cupido minimus

THE CATERPILLARS OF THE SMALL BLUE feed on only one species of wild flower – a member of the pea family called kidney vetch. No kidney vetch equals no small blue – it is a simple equation. It is vital that the chalk grasslands and coastal dunes where kidney vetch grows are maintained for the survival of this butterfly.

This is our smallest species, and its numbers have declined throughout most of its range. The first adults of the year emerge in May, with the possibility of another generation appearing before the end of the summer, especially in the south. Their short lives are spent basking, feeding and looking for a mate.

COLOURING

The butterfly in the main picture (left) is a male: he has a sprinkling of blue scales which the female lacks. Both sexes have silvery-grey undersides interrupted with black spots (below). The picture shows the beautifully rounded shape of the wings, too.

LOOKING FOR SMALL BLUES

For the very reason that they are small, these butterflies can be tricky to find. Why not set yourself the challenge of trying to spot the tiny eggs – laid singly at the base of kidney-vetch flower buds – or the caterpillars as well!

LIVING IN COLONIES

By late afternoon, groups of small blues roost headdown on tall grasses. These butterflies live in small colonies, rarely venturing far from where they hatched as caterpillars. From time to time, an individual will stray from the area and, if the conditions are right, will form part of a new colony.

SMALL COPPER
Lycaena phlaeas

THE SMALL COPPER'S WINGS dazzle in the sun as the butterfly circles a flower as it feeds. This one is taking nectar from ragwort, one of its preferred flowers along with common fleabane, mint and thistles. The male defends its territory aggressively, chasing away any insect that dares to approach. It is a seemingly fearless bundle of energy that spends its two- to three-week lifespan feeding, fighting and mating.

The small copper is resident throughout most of the British Isles and Europe where it flies in one, two or three broods from late April until October, if the weather is warm enough.

OTHER COPPERS

The UK was once lucky enough to be home to the large copper (centre below) as well as the small copper. Colonies depended on the watery fenlands of eastern England where its caterpillars fed on great waterdock. Over 100 years ago, the fens were drained for agricultural purposes and the large copper became extinct. It is now one of the 10 coppers found in continental Europe along with species such as the scarce copper (below left) and the sooty copper (below right).

Scarce copper

Sooty copper

Large copper

COURTSHIP

The male small copper seems to live life in the fast lane. It dashes around looking for females and, once one is found, there is a swift courtship followed by mating. The female takes her time – slowly fluttering and testing different leaves in order to find the perfect egg-laying sites.

FACTFILE
FOUND: Open, flowery
grasslands, heathlands
& scrubby areas
FLIES: April–October
CATERPILLARS FEED ON:
Sorrel or dock
WINGSPAN: 26–40 mm
FAMILY: Coppers

SMALL HEATH

Coenonympha pamphilus

THIS DIMINUTIVE BROWN butterfly is easy to confuse with the meadow brown and the gatekeeper, but it is smaller, hairier and always rests with its wings closed. Although wing colours vary between individuals, generally the female is paler than the male. Look for groups of males gathering in shorter grassland or sheltered areas where they battle it out to impress females.

The small heath is more widespread than its close relation the large heath, but maybe not for long. Its numbers have been in steep decline as its grassland habitats disappear, with land being repurposed for farming and house-building.

PREDATORS

Grasslands are home to many tiny and often fierce creatures, such as the crab spider below. It is a fearsome predator which can change its colour to match its surroundings. The small heath butterfly makes a tasty morsel for carnivores such as this.

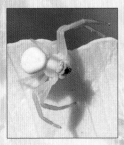

FROM CATERPILLAR TO CHRYSALIS

After mating, the female small heath lays her barrel-shaped eggs singly on blades of grass. The caterpillars that hatch stay lowdown in their grassy habitat, coming out to feed at night. As they grow, they shed their skin four times, with each new stage of their caterpillar life being referred to as an instar.

Below you can see the fifth instar as it transforms into a chrysalis. It hangs headdown attached by silken threads to a dead grass stem, where it takes three weeks to complete its transformation into an adult.

SMALL PEARL-BORDERED FRITILLARY
Boloria selene

THE "PEARLS" ARE THE MILKY-WHTE spots on the hindwings, while the *Boloria* of its scientific name comes from the Greek for fishing net, referring to its orange and black upperwing pattern. Look for this, our smallest fritillary, gliding through damp grassland habitats from June to July or nectaring from flowers such as bluebells, ragged-Robin and common bird's-foot-trefoil.

Where have all the small pearl-bordered fritillaries gone? There has been a rapid decline in numbers of this and the closely related pearl-bordered fritillary. The restoration of areas of bracken where violets grow will help the survival of these species.

PEARL-BORDERED FRITILLARY

This fritillary flies early in the year, from late April or early May. It inhabits bracken slopes and freshly-cut woodland clearings where violets grow in profusion in warm conditions and on which its caterpillars feed.

Trying to distinguish this from the small pearl-bordered fritillary is a challenge. The wing undersides are helpful here. See if you can make out a duck's face in the pattern of the pearl-bordered fritillary. Also, its "pearls" are edged with orange chevrons, while those of the small pearl-bordered fritillary are edged with black.

CATERPILLARS

Small pearl-bordered fritillary caterpillars moult several times before hibernating. They wake up the following spring to feed on violet leaves and complete their life cycle. This is a fully-grown caterpillar, complete with bristles and spikes.

Pearl-bordered fritillary

Small pearl-bordered fritillary

FACTFILE
FOUND: Moors,
woodland clearings &
damp grasslands
FLIES: June–July
CATERPILLARS FEED ON:
Violets
WINGSPAN: 35–44 mm
FAMILY: Fritillaries

SMALL SKIPPER

Thymelicus sylvestris

FLASHES OF ORANGE may be the first signs that you are in small skipper country. This golden-orange butterfly emerges in June and lives in colonies in tall grasslands and open wooded areas of England and Wales. Its name is misleading, for it is small in relation only to the large skipper and not to the Essex, Lulworth and grizzled skippers.

Flying requires energy, so the small skipper visits flower-rich grassy areas and feeds from plants – especially purple ones – with multiple flowerheads, such as thistles and clovers. At night and in bad weather it roosts on tall grasses.

EGG-LAYING

The female small skipper pumps out between three and five eggs at a time into the curled-up velvety blades of grasses such as Yorkshire-fog (shown below). Like most butterflies, she chooses the spots on which to lay her eggs with care.

FLYING STYLE

This butterfly family is named after its skipping flight style. The thick body of the small skipper contains powerful flight muscles. These enable it to move rapidly around its grassy habitat, especially the males which are more active than the females.

MALES

This is one of the five golden skippers found in the UK. They all perch with their forewings at angles to their hindwings. Male skippers differ from females in having a thin black line of scent scales in the middle of their forewings (below).

FACTFILE
FOUND: Anywhere in
the country or towns
FLIES: March–
September
CATERPILLARS FEED ON:
Nettle
WINGSPAN: 42–52 mm
FAMILY: Vanessids

SMALL TORTOISESHELL

Aglais urticae

THIS POPULAR GARDEN BUTTERFLY may be seen flying at any time between March and October. The *Aglais* in its scientific name means "beautiful", which this butterfly surely is, and *urticae* is the Latin name of the nettle on which its caterpillars feed.

Its striking colours are easy to spot as it basks in the sun or drinks nectar from flowers. There are two generations each year, with butterflies from the second one overwintering as adults. This brood concentrates on building up its energy reserves before finding sheltered places in which to hibernate, such as sheds, woodpiles and hollowed-out trees.

CATERPILLARS

The female small tortoiseshell lays large batches of eggs on tender young nettle leaves. On hatching, the caterpillars build web-like tents, inside which they feed and grow, emerging to bask or to move to fresh leaves.

KNOW YOUR TORTOISESHELLS

There were once significant numbers of large tortoiseshells in the UK. Reports of this butterfly are now rare and limited to a few sightings annually in southern England. It is similar, but larger, than the small tortoiseshell, with no white markings on its upperwings.

Below right is the scarce tortoiseshell – an even rarer European migrant species. The black border running along the outer edge of its upperwings is wider and darker than that of the small tortoiseshell.

Large tortoiseshell

Scarce tortoiseshell

SMALL WHITE
Pieris rapae

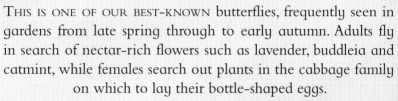

THIS IS ONE OF OUR BEST-KNOWN butterflies, frequently seen in gardens from late spring through to early autumn. Adults fly in search of nectar-rich flowers such as lavender, buddleia and catmint, while females search out plants in the cabbage family on which to lay their bottle-shaped eggs.

Human travel around the globe led to the accidental introduction of the small white from Europe to North America around 1860 and from there to New Zealand in the 20th century. As the farming of cabbage crops intensified around the world, the small white butterfly continued its inexorable spread.

PREDATORS

Small white populations can be affected by natural enemies in the form of parasitic wasps, which hatch out and feed on the insides of the caterpillars. House sparrows prey on small white caterpillars, too.

LARGE OR SMALL WHITE?

Collectively, large and small whites are known as cabbage whites, for the obvious reason that their caterpillars feed on plants in the cabbage family. The two species are very similar – both have creamy pale underwings and black spots on their upperwings.

To be certain of which one you are looking at, check the colouring on the uppersides of the wings. The large white has darker, deeper black wing tips while those of the small white are paler and smaller.

Small white

Large white

SPECKLED WOOD

Pararge aegeria

DAMP DAPPLED WOODS are the perfect places for spotting this common brown butterfly, which may be seen any time between March and October. The speckled wood's day starts with basking in the sun until its muscles are warm enough for flying. At night and in unsettled weather, it roosts high in the treetops.

If you see a speckled wood, it is likely to be a male. He is quick to guard his territory – usually a sunny spot on bracken or bramble bushes – which he will defend fiercely from intruders. If another male approaches, the two will spiral upwards into the air until the victor (usually the first male) returns to his perch.

CAMOUFLAGE

The dark and light colouring of the speckled wood's wings camouflage it perfectly in shady woodland. The female is slightly larger than the male and has bolder markings, yet much of its brief life is spent out of sight high in the forest canopy.

HIBERNATION

When the weather turns cold, butterflies hibernate. Most do so as caterpillars, but some see out the winter as eggs, chrysalises or adults. Only the speckled wood hibernates either as a caterpillar (below) or as a chrysalis (far right).

CHRYSALIS

Below (left), a speckled wood caterpillar is about to shed its skin one final time to reveal a protective case called a chrysalis (right). Inside this, the caterpillar's body breaks down to form a soupy mixture, which transforms into an adult butterfly.

FACTFILE

FOUND: Woodlands, hedgerows

FLIES: March–June & July–October

CATERPILLARS FEED ON: Woodland grasses

WINGSPAN: 46–56 mm

FAMILY: Browns

FACTFILE

FOUND: Only in East Anglia in low-lying marshlands called fens

FLIES: May–July; Aug

CATERPILLARS FEED ON: Milk-parsley

WINGSPAN: 80–90 mm

FAMILY: Swallowtails

SWALLOWTAIL

Papilio machaon britannicus

THE MARSHY FENLANDS of East Anglia are home to this, our largest butterfly and the only member of the swallowtail family found in the UK. Although it is colourful and showy, it is not a common sight as it spends its life among rather inaccessible reedbeds and ditches. This is where milk-parsley grows – the only plant its caterpillars eat and on which its survival depends.

The first generation of swallowtails flies between May and July, with a possible second brood emerging in August. Sometimes, the adults sip nectar while flapping their wings – hummingbird style – to prevent their large bodies from weighing down flowerheads.

SCARCE SWALLOWTAIL

This is one of the 10 European swallowtail species. Like the others, it is large and colourful with a long tail. There have been rare UK sightings, when individuals may have been blown off course or accidentally imported.

CATERPILLAR DEFENCES

When young, a swallowtail caterpillar is camouflaged to look like a bird dropping. As its grows and sheds its skin, it becomes bright green, black and orange. Being more visible to predators, it protects itself by rising up and extending a forked orange tentacle on its head and emitting a strong smell.

Despite these clever defences, many caterpillars still fall prey to spiders, small mammals and birds such as reed warblers (below). If they survive these dangers, they may still be killed by parasitic wasps and flies.

127

VANESSIDS

THESE COLOURFUL BUTTERFLIES are frequent garden visitors between spring and autumn. The vanessids belong to a huge family called Nymphalidae, which numbers about 6,000 species and which also include the fritillaries and browns.

A CLOSER LOOK at a PAINTED LADY

Wavy wing edges

Forewing

Hindwing

Veins

Eye-spots

Colourful wing uppersides

Teardrop-shaped antennae

Hairy eyes

2 pairs of legs used for walking

EGGS

The eggs are barrel-shaped and ribbed. Some species lay them singly, others in clusters or batches.

CATERPILLARS

Nettles are a popular foodplant for spiny vanessid caterpillars. Some spin webs in which they hide and feed.

CHRYSALISES

Each chrysalis hangs head-down from a plant stem. Certain species have gold and silver spots on the cases.

VANESSID BUTTERFLY GALLERY

The Camberwell beauty, large and scarce tortoiseshell and map butterflies shown below are rare migrants to the UK. The rest are found both here and in parts of continental Europe.

MAP	SMALL TORTOISESHELL	COMMA

Wavy or angled wing edges like these are characteristic of vanessids.

RED ADMIRAL	CAMBERWELL BEAUTY	PAINTED LADY

Vanessids are powerful fliers and some, like these species, migrate long distances.

LARGE TORTOISESHELL	PEACOCK	SCARCE TORTOISESHELL

The dark wing undersides camouflage these butterflies when they are at rest.

WALL
Lasiommata megera

BASKING IN THE SUN on stony paths or earthy banks, the wall butterfly uses the warmth from the ground to heat up its flight muscles. These are nervous butterflies which are easily disturbed. Their lifespan is a mere three or four days, during which time they feed, bask, roost and reproduce.

The butterfly on the right is a female. Males have larger brown patches including scent scales on their uppersides. Although the wall is widespread throughout Europe, its numbers in the UK have declined significantly in the past 50 years, especially inland, possibly owing to pollution and the use of fertilisers.

CATERPILLARS

There are two, sometimes three, generations of wall butterflies each year. The females lay their eggs close to bare or broken ground on a variety of grasses, such as bents, cock's-foot and Yorkshire-fog, which provide warm conditions for the caterpillars.

Here you can see the stages of the caterpillar's growth. It sheds its skin three times to give its body room to expand, with each stage between moults being known as an instar. The caterpillar is just over 2 mm on hatching and grows to over 6 mm long.

UNDERSIDES

When the wall rests with its wings closed, it keeps the large eye-spots on its forewings on display at first. This helps to fool predators into thinking it is a much larger and more dangerous animal. Within seconds, the forewings are hidden behind the hindwings, helping to camouflage it against its background.

FACTFILE

FOUND: Various dry
grasslands including
coastland & quarries
FLIES: April–October
CATERPILLARS FEED ON:
A variety of grasses
WINGSPAN: 44–46 mm
FAMILY: Browns

WHITE ADMIRAL

Limenitis camilla

A WALK IN THE WOODS between July and August may be rewarded with the sight of this handsome butterfly as it flaps and glides gracefully through the trees. When its upperwings catch the light, they have a metallic sheen to them which contrasts with the striking gold and white pattern of its underwings.

White admirals are found throughout Europe and in the south and east of the UK. They spend their lives flitting from flower to flower along woodland rides and glades, with brambles being a particular favourite. Although in recent years the white admiral has been found further north, its overall numbers are falling.

COMPETITION FOR FOOD

Dangling strands of honeysuckle in shady woods are the perfect place to find white admiral caterpillars. However, such plants are susceptible to browsing from the growing number of roe deer (below).

CATERPILLARS

Newly hatched white admiral caterpillars shed their skins four times before they are fully grown. They have a strange habit of storing their droppings – known as frass – at the end of leaves as a way to deter predators such as beetles and spiders.

NEW ADULTS

This white admiral has just emerged from its chrysalis. It hangs upside-down while it waits for its wings to expand and dry out, allowing it to fly. For most butterflies, this process takes between 30 minutes and two hours.

FACTFILE

FOUND: Woodlands,
hedgerows & fields
where elm trees grow

FLIES: July–August

CATERPILLARS FEED ON:
Species of elm trees

WINGSPAN: 36 mm

FAMILY: Hairstreaks

WHITE-LETTER HAIRSTREAK

Satyrium w-album

BOTH THE SCIENTIFIC and the English names of this small butterfly refer to the white "W" mark on the underside of each hindwing. Its uppersides are a dark chocolate brown, yet these are rarely seen because it always settles with its wings closed.

White-letter hairstreaks fly in one brood from June to August. Most of their short lives are spent among the treetops, where they feed on sticky honeydew coating the leaves of trees, especially ash, lime and maple. Look for males engaged in acrobatic territorial battles – circling up into the air around the tops of elm trees, silhouetted against the sun's light.

ELM TREES

These are wych elm leaves – one of the elms on which hairstreak caterpillars feed. In the 1970s, about 25 million elms died in the UK from Dutch elm disease. This led to the loss of many white-letter hairstreak colonies. However, some survived by feeding on young elm shoots.

EGGS

Looking for white-letter hairstreak eggs may be easier than spotting the elusive adults. The female lays them singly on elm twigs in sunny, sheltered places. A caterpillar grows inside each egg, remaining there for nine months from July until spring when elm leaves emerge.

BLACK HAIRSTREAK

This rare butterfly looks very similar to the white-letter hairstreak but it is a more golden colour and has black spots and no "W" mark on its hindwings. It flies from late June to July in a few woodland areas of England where blackthorn grows.

WHITES & YELLOWS

COLOUR IS THE KEY FEATURE of this family, commonly called whites and yellows and with the scientific name Pieridae. The markings often vary slightly between males and females and between the generations if there is more than one brood a year.

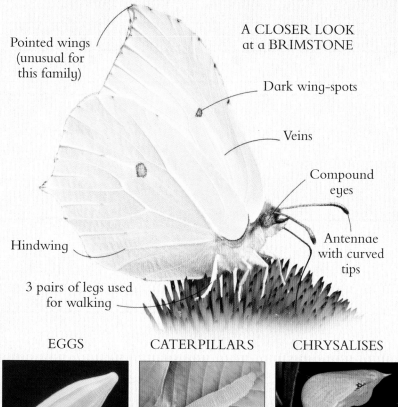

A CLOSER LOOK at a BRIMSTONE

Pointed wings (unusual for this family)

Dark wing-spots

Veins

Compound eyes

Antennae with curved tips

Hindwing

3 pairs of legs used for walking

EGGS

The tall, bottle-shaped eggs are unmistakable. All species lay their eggs singly, except for the large white.

CATERPILLARS

Wrinkled green caterpillars are typical of whites and yellows. They feed on plants in the cabbage family.

CHRYSALISES

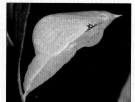

Most chrysalises of whites and yellows are upright, each secured onto a plant stem by a single thread.

WHITES AND YELLOWS BUTTERFLY GALLERY

Of the 1,275 species worldwide, there are over 50 whites and yellows in Europe, with six resident in the UK (marked with a ★). Many already here are joined annually by migrating butterflies.

LARGE WHITE ★

CLOUDED YELLOW

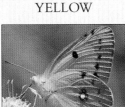

BATH WHITE

These three species migrate here, although the bath white is rare.

BLACK-VEINED WHITE

ORANGE-TIP ★

GREEN-VEINED WHITE ★

Some whites and yellows hold their wings half-open to absorb warmth from the sun.

WOOD WHITE ★

PALE CLOUDED YELLOW

CLEOPATRA

Others – like these three – are rarely seen with their wings open.

FACTFILE

FOUND: Woodland
rides & undercliffs

FLIES: May–June &
August

CATERPILLARS FEED ON:
Vetches

WINGSPAN: 36–48 mm

FAMILY: Whites/Yellows

WOOD WHITE
Leptidea sinapis

NO OTHER BRITISH BUTTERFLY flies in the same way as a wood white. It has the air of some woodland fairy as it dances along the undergrowth at around knee level. Its long, oval wings beat slowly as it moves between nectar sources or searches for a mate.

These delicate insects may be seen in one or two broods from May until August. They need woods with open spaces where plants in the pea family – the food source for the caterpillars – have enough light to grow. The female wood white tests the leaves by tapping them with her antennae and feet before laying each egg singly on the leaf undersides if they prove suitable.

COURTSHIP

What female wood white could fail to be impressed by a male swaying his antennae and proboscis in front of her? A receptive female bends her body towards the male. His display is wasted on any female that has already mated.

CHRYSALIS

When fully-grown, the caterpillar travels away from its food source and attaches itself to a stem with a thread. Here it transforms into a chrysalis which is only 1.5 cm long. It will hibernate until May when the adult butterfly is ready to emerge.

CRYPTIC WOOD WHITE

In 2001, what were thought to be wood white colonies in parts of Ireland were found to be a new species called the cryptic wood white. The best way to tell the two species apart is by analysing their genetic make-up or DNA!

GLOSSARY

ABDOMEN
The part of a butterfly's body containing organs involved in respiration, digestion and reproduction.

ABERRATION
A butterfly with colouring that differs from others of the same species.

ANTENNA
One of the long feelers on a butterfly's head which detect scents and help it to balance.

APHID
A small insect that feeds on the sap of plants.

BROOD
A single generation of a species of butterfly.

CANOPY
The upper leafy layer of trees.

CATERPILLAR
The small, worm-like creature that forms the second stage in a butterfly's development.

CHRYSALIS
The third stage in a butterfly's development during which it transforms from a caterpillar into an adult.

CLUB
The thick end part of a butterfly's antenna.

COLONY
A group of butterflies that live and interact with each other.

COMPOUND EYE
An eye common to insects with many light-sensitive units, each with a lens.

DNA
Short for deoxyribonucleic acid – molecules found in cells which carry instructions for what makes animals unique.

DOWNLAND
Grassy hillsides found in southern England formed from chalk rock.

ENTOMOLOGIST
A person who studies insects.

FAMILY
A group of organisms that share characteristics.

FENLAND
A marshy low-lying area of land.

FOREWING
One of the top pair of wings attached to the thorax closest to the head.

FRASS
Insect droppings.

GENUS
A group of organisms that are very closely related to each other.

HABITAT
A particular environment in which animals live and plants grows.

HIBERNATION
The sleep-like state which some animals enter in order to survive the winter.

HINDWING
One of the lower or rear pair of wings attached to the thorax.

HONEYDEW
A sweet, sticky substance covering leaves and stems, produced by aphids.

HOST PLANT
The name for a plant on which a caterpillar depends in order to grow.

INSTAR
The stages of a caterpillar's life between each moult.

LARVA
Another term for a caterpillar.

LEPIDOPTERA
The scientific term for butterflies and moths.

LEPIDOPTERIST
Someone who studies butterflies and moths.

METAMORPHOSIS
The transformation of an animal into different stages in order to reach adulthood.

MIGRATION
The seasonal movement of animals from one place to another.

MOULT
The process by which

caterpillars shed their skins in order to grow.

NECTAR
A sweet liquid produced by insect-pollinated flowers.

NECTARING
The act of drinking nectar from flowers.

NUTRIENT
A substance taken in by animals and plants for growth and metabolism.

OVERWINTER
To survive the colder months. Butterflies overwinter in one of their four life stages.

OVIPOSITOR
The tube or egg-laying organ of a female insect.

PARASITIC
Parasitic organisms live on or in other species, taking from them what they need to live and grow.

PHEROMONE
A chemical released by animals to affect the behaviour of other animals of the same species.

POLLEN
Fine grains produced by male flowers in order to fertilise female flowers.

POLLINATION
The transfer of pollen from male to female flowers so that seeds can form.

POLLINATOR
An animal that moves pollen from the male to the female part of a flower.

PREDATOR
An animal that hunts other animals for food.

PROBOSCIS
An adult butterfly's feeding tube or tongue, used to drink liquids.

PUDDLING
When butterflies (usually male) drink water and salts from wet ground.

PUPA
Another term for a chrysalis.

PUPATE
The process in which a caterpillar transforms into a chrysalis.

RANGE
The total area in which a particular species is found.

RESIDENT
A species found living all year round in a particular geographical location.

ROOSTING
When butterflies rest at night or in bad weather.

SAP
The energy-giving liquid flowing through plants, made up of water, sugars and minerals.

SCENT GLAND
Special scales on male butterfly wings that release substances, known as pheromones, to attract females.

SCIENTIFIC NAME
The two-part name – usually derived from Latin or Greek – that identifies a particular species.

SPECIES
A group of organisms, such as plants and animals, that share the same characteristics and can reproduce with each other.

STRIDULATION
The sound produced by animals when they move hard body parts together.

SUBSPECIES
A species that lives apart from others of the same species and has slightly different characteristics.

THORAX
The middle part of an insect's body to which the legs and wings are attached.

TOXIN
A poison produced by a plant or an animal.

TUSSOCK
A patch of grass that is thicker and longer than the grass around it.

UNDERSIDE
The side of a butterfly's wings seen when closed.

UPPERSIDE
The side of a butterfly's wings seen when held open.

VEIN
One of the tubes running through a butterfly's wings.

INDEX

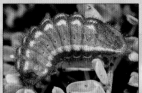

ACKNOWLEDGEMENTS

WITH THANKS TO

Sunita Gahir – Prepress designer
Yolanta Motylinska – Production adviser
Penny Phillips – Proofreader

PICTURE CREDITS

Key: t = top; m = middle; b = bottom; l = left; c = centre; r = right; bcl = bottom centre left;
bcr = bottom centre right; bla = bottom left above; blb = bottom left below

© Andrew Fusek-Peters
6; 143 br

© Peter Eeles
Cover c; 12 l; 13 tl, tc; 15 bl, bc; 16 bl, bc, br; 17 tr, tc, ml, mc, mr, br; 18 bc; 20 bl, bc; 21; 22 bl, bc, br; 23 tr, mc, bl,
bc; 26; 28 bl, br; 31 bl, bc; 33 bcl, bcr; 35 br, bc; 37 b; 40 bl, bc, br; 44 bl, bc, br; 45; 46 br; 47; 49 blb; 52 bl, br; 53
ml, mc, mr, br; 60 bcl, bcr, br; 61; 62 bc; 63; 65 bcr; 66 bl, bc; 67; 68 t, bl, bc, br; 69 tl, tr, ml, mc, mr, bl, br; 71 bl;
72 bl, bcl, bcr, br; 74; 75 bl; 76 bl; bc; 81 bcl, bcr, br; 82 br; 83; 85 bl, bc; 88 bc, br; 94; 95 bl, bcl, bcr, br; 96 bl, bc,
br; 97; 100 br; 103 bc; 104; 105 bl, bcl, bcr; 106 bl; 108 t, bl, bc, br; 109 tl, tm, bl, bc; 111 bl, bc, br; 112 bcl; 114;
115 bcl, bcr, br; 116 bl, bcl, bcr, br; 117; 121 bc, br; 124 bcl, bcr, br; 126; 127 bc; 128 bl, bc, br; 129 mc, bl, br; 130
bl, bcl, bcr, bc, br; 131; 132 bc, br; 133; 134; 135 bc, br; 136 bl, bc, br; 137 tr, bc, br; 139 bl, bc, br; 144 tl, tc, tr, bc

© Martin Warren
49 blt

© Shutterstock
9 tc, bc; 10 b; 11 tl, tr, bl, br; 16 t; 18 t; 23 cr, br; 25 bl; 42 tl, tc, bl, bc, br; 43 ml, bc; 46 bl, bcl, bcr; 52 t; 57 bl, br;
59 br; 69 bc; 75 br; 86; 93 br; 95 t; 103 br; 105 bl; 118 bc; 122 bl; 127 bl; 132 bl

© Alan Buckingham
20 br; 25 bc; 55 br; 78 bc

All other images © Fine Feather Press

MARSH FRITILLARY p82

MEADOW BROWN p84

ORANGE-TIP p88

PAINTED LADY p90

PEACOCK p92

PURPLE EMPEROR p94

PURPLE HAIRSTREAK p96

RED ADMIRAL p100